STARS OF WONDER

FIVE CHRISTMAS PLAYS
FOR CHILDREN

By

BRIAN MOUNTFORD

IN MEMORY OF JENNY BOSTOCK

whose talent as a producer brought the
first three of these plays to life

CONTENTS

Tufton Books
Faith House
7 Tufton Street
London
SW1P 3QN

ISBN 0-85191-314-8

First published in Great Britain 1997 by Tufton Books (Church Union Publications)

© Brian Mountford 1997

1 3 5 7 9 10 8 6 4 2

Acknowledgements

© Brian Mountford
"Dance, dance and praise the Lord"

© Salvationist Publishing Supplies/Copy Care
"It was on a starry night" by Joy Webb
from *Merrily to Bethlehem* © A. & C. Black

"The Shepherd's Play" is based on the second shepherd's pageant featured in *Everyman and Medieval Miracle Plays* edited by A C Cawley and published by Everyman Paperbacks.

Cover design: "Russian Christmas"
This artwork was produced by Catherine Brighty for Shelter, the National Campaign for Homeless People. For more information on Shelter's work please write to: Shelter, 88 Old Street, London, CE1V 9HU or phone 0171 505 2000

Typeset by Phoenix Photosetting, Chatham, Kent
Printed and bound in Great Britain by Ashford Colour Press, Gosport, Hampshire

STARS OF WONDER
FIVE CHRISTMAS PLAYS FOR CHILDREN

These Christmas plays for children, by Brian Mountford, were written for performance by the Sunday School of the Church of St Mary the Virgin, Oxford on the Sunday before Christmas, and also at the Christmas Eve Crib Service. They are designed to be flexible enough to include children from a wide age range - from three year old non-speaking angels, to eight year olds with just one or two lines, and eleven to thirteen year olds taking larger parts. They can be used as a part of worship, or on their own.

They can be used in schools just as easily as in churches.

A competent pianist is needed to accompany the songs, and it is helpful in some of the plays to have extra recorded musical effects.

THE CAT'S CRADLE

CAST
Nine (Narrator, 5m/f, 2m, 1f), plus angels and wise men
(non-speaking).

AGE RANGE
3 - 12

APPROXIMATE RUNNING TIME
20 minutes

MUSIC
'The Cat and the Mouse' Carol Number 8 in 'Merrily to
Bethlehem' (Black).
'Baa, baa, black sheep'
Heavenly music (piano or organ)
'Away in a manger'
'We three kings'

SET
Bare Stage, with props as instructed

SYNOPSIS
A mouse, a rat, a cat, and a spider, residents of the stable at
Bethlehem, give their version of the nativity story.

KNOCK, KNOCK, WHO'S THERE?

CAST
Eleven (Narrator, 5m, 2f, 3m/f) plus many non-speaking
roles.

AGE RANGE
3 - 12

APPROXIMATE RUNNING TIME
20 - 25 minutes

MUSIC
'Dance, dance, and praise the Lord' (in text)
'I saw three ships'
'We wish you a merry Christmas'
'It was on a starry night', 7 in 'Merrily to Bethlehem'
'Good King Wencelas'

SET
Bare stage, with props as instructed

SYNOPSIS
In the medieval court, the King, his jester, and his courtiers
are having a great party. Fed up with frivolity, the King
wishes to know the secret of Christmas. The actors perform
a short nativity play that so fascinates the King that he wants
to meet Christ. He is persuaded to take food to a poor
peasant, where he discovers the truth of the saying that
'inasmuch as you do it unto the least of these my brethren,
you do it unto me'.

YULETIDE TV NEWS

CAST
Nineteen (7m, 4f, 8 m/f)

AGE RANGE
5 - 13

APPROXIMATE RUNNING TIME
20 - 25 minutes

MUSIC
Recorded: dramatic 'ITN' type music
Recorded excerpts of Christmas music from Handel's
'Messiah'
Carols:
'When Joseph was an old man'
'While Shepherds Watched'   } (or personal choice)
'We Three Kings'
'Unto us a child is born'

SET
Desk and chairs to suggest TV Studio. Otherwise bare stage,
with props as instructed.

SYNOPSIS
A TV News Channel features the Christmas story with
reports from various correspondents and interviews with
the main characters.
Music played between the items has a distinctive Christmas
theme.

MAK THE THIEF

CAST
Seven (2f, 5m/f)

AGE RANGE
11 - 13 (Equally viable for 13 - 15 or adults)

APPROXIMATE RUNNING TIME
30 minutes

MUSIC
The 'Sans Day Carol' and the 'Sussex Carol'.

SET
A bare stage, with props as instructed.

SYNOPSIS
The shepherds around Bethlehem are troubled by a sheep stealer who pretends that a stolen sheep is his wife's new baby. The story that unfolds provides a humorous and amusing contrast to the actual nativity of Christ.

CHRISTMAS CABARET

CAST
Four (2m, 1f, 1 Reader m/f), plus child participants from the
audience

AGE RANGE
The three main parts are taken by adults.

APPROXIMATE RUNNING TIME
30 - 35 minutes

MUSIC
Free choice of Carols
'Rudolph the red nosed reindeer'
Incidental music, either recorded or live

SET
Bare stage, with props as instructed

SYNOPSIS
Four entertainers use a box of props to illustrate the story
and traditions of Christmas. They create a pantomime
atmosphere with much amusement and audience
participation.

THE CAT'S CRADLE

Characters: Narrator, a mouse, a cat, a rat, and a spider. St Luke, Mary, Joseph, Shepherds, Wise Men, Angels, and Innkeeper. Other children can dress as animals.

The play begins with 'The Cat and the Mouse Carol', Number 8 in 'Merrily to Bethlehem' (Black).
All the children come on stage to sing this. Then they disperse to their places. If it is performed in a church, Mary and Joseph should be positioned in a distant corner, the shepherds visible stage right, the angels hidden by the altar, the innkeeper stage left, and the other characters at the back of the church.
The four animals enter from the back. The mouse is juggling, the cat is playing with wool, making a cat's cradle, the rat dances, and the spider makes patterns in the air with a silk scarf.

Narrator   Once upon a time, two thousand years ago, in a stable in Bethlehem, there lived four friends: a cat, a mouse, a rat, and a spider. They had their own beds in different parts of the stable:

Mouse   the mouse and the rat under the straw on the ground,

Spider   the spider in the crevices of the rock,

Cat   and the cat - well, the cat was usually out at night! And in the day slept wherever there was space.

Narrator   The other animals - the donkeys and cows -

didn't mind sharing their stable at all. Rat and mouse nibbled the seeds from the hay, the cat always had his meals out, and, frankly, they weren't even aware that spiders existed.

Rat

The town where they lived was a very ordinary place; nothing exciting ever happened there. In fact, the cat had been thinking of moving.

Cat

It can get very boring out here in the sticks, Rat. I think I'm more of a town cat. Jerusalem's where it's at, Rat.

Narrator

Each of the four friends had a hobby.

Mouse

(Giving a juggling exhibition)
Mouse was good at juggling, and earned a few shekels in the market place entertaining passers by.

Spider

Spider liked to spin, and had just made a silk scarf for his auntie. *(Performs a spidery dance waving silk scarves through the air)*

Rat

Rat was a dancer - an ecstatic dancer - a cross between a break-dancer and a Kossack dancer. When Rat got going he could hold an audience for half an hour. *(Rat gives a dancing demonstration)*

Cat

The cat liked to play with wool: he was still a kitten at heart. *(Goes through the 'cat's cradle'*

routine, assisted by another child)
His speciality was the cat's cradle.

Narrator   But let them tell you their own story.
(Each animal comes centre stage to say his rhyme)

Mouse   I guess you're wond'ring who I am,
I'm Maccabeus the mouse,
And I live here in Bethlehem -
This stable is my house.

I earn my cheese by making jokes
And juggling with deception.
I'm good at making babies laugh
When they've got indigestion.

Cat   I'm Carmel Black, the Bethlem cat,
I pad from door to door,
I know each shadow of the town,
And go to bed at four.

Nothing goes unnoticed here;
I am the stable's ears and eyes;
I watch the turning of the year,
And see the movements in the skies.

Last week I saw a golden star,
Appearing in the east.
It burned and sparkled like a fire,
And frightened all the beasts.

Spider	I've got eight legs, and like to spin;

Spider   I've got eight legs, and like to spin;
My name is Simon. I'm a spider.
Last night I had a curious dream;
I saw a donkey and his rider.

And round the rider's saintly head,
A ring of light shone like the moon.
And then I heard a voice that said,
'The Prince of Peace is coming soon'.

I'm going to weave a special gift,
Of cloth made with the finest thread,
And bead it with the morning mist,
And hang it by his royal bed.

Rat   Something's up. There's something wrong.
I've listened to the shepherds chat:
They say they've heard a heavenly song.
By the way *(bows)* ... I'm Reuben Rat.

King Herod's in an awful stew
About the rumours being spread.
He thinks there'll be a palace coup -
His ugly face is raging red.

A prophet, with a hairy chin,
Has said the time is drawing near
For God to put an end to sin,
And that his son will soon be here.

So what do you think of that?

Narrator	Carmel, Maccabeus, Reuben and Simon all realised that something strange was happening in their small town of Bethlehem. But what was it all about?
St Luke	My name is Luke, and the answer is written in my Gospel. About the year 'nought' the Roman Emperor decided to make a list of all the people who lived in his empire. Every single person had to go to the city where they had been born to place their name on the roll at the town hall. *(Joseph and Mary walk from their distant corner to the centre of the stage, where there is a chair for Mary with a manger in front of it)* Joseph and Mary had to travel a hundred miles from Nazareth to Bethlehem, the City of David, because Joseph was of the same family as David.
Cat	It was a long a dangerous journey which took many days through hard and hilly countryside. Joseph didn't want to go at all.
Joseph	Who do these Romans think they are? Don't they realise that Mary is in no fit state to travel. She's going to have a baby and can't walk all that way. Hiring a donkey will cost me all my savings.
Narrator	But he had no choice. They must go to Bethlehem or end up in prison.

Rat	When they arrived the sun was setting behind the hills in a furnace of red and orange light.
Spider	They were exhausted and hungry, and didn't know where they were going to stay. *(At this point the audience, which has been primed beforehand, makes the sounds of the market place, including jangling the money in their pockets).*
Narrator	*(More audience market-place noise)* There were people everywhere: talking, shouting, selling, herding sheep through the narrow streets, changing money from one currency to another.
Rat	Mary, who felt anxious in the strange place, saw a little mouse juggling in the market place, and burst out laughing. *(Mary starts to giggle)*
Mary	But where are we going to sleep?
Cat	I know a place. Just follow me. It's my master's guesthouse.
Narrator	*(Mary, Joseph and the Cat move in a circle round the stage until they come to the Innkeeper)* Round a corner, down an alley, through an archway they went, pushing and shoving in the fading light.
Innkeeper	I'm terribly sorry, my dear. There isn't a bed in the place. The whole town's gone crazy. The

baker's run out of bread, and there are people sleeping in the streets.

Narrator   When he saw how tired Mary was, and that she was going to have a baby, he felt sorry for her.

Innkeeper   But I suppose you and your husband could sleep in the stable, if you don't mind the smell.

Narrator   During that night the baby was born, and Joseph took the tiny child, washed him in the water trough, wrapped him in a white towel, and laid him in the manger.

Cat   It was an extraordinary night, when the moon shone so bright that its mountains and craters stood out like great bruises.

Spider   On the hills outside the city the shepherds were having a singsong around their fire.

Shepherds   *(Sing 'Baa, baa, black sheep', or, if the children are older, some other suitable song)*

Narrator   And as they sang they thought they heard other music - heavenly music.
(Angelic music - 'In Paradisum' from Fauré's 'Requiem' works well - as the angels enter and dance in a circle around the stage, while the Narrator continues:)

Narrator	Just at that moment the moon emerged from behind a cloud in a burst of uncanny brightness.
Mouse	The wind whooshed like the sound of a flock of geese fanning through the air. The shepherds stopped singing and looked up at the sky afraid.
Rat	It seemed that the great voice came from out of the clouds:
Voice	*(From pulpit or offstage)* 'Fear not: for, behold, I bring you good tidings of great joy, which shall be to all people. For unto you is born this day in the City of David a Saviour, which is Christ the Lord. Ye shall find the babe wrapped in swaddling clothes, lying in a manger.'
Cat	As soon as the voice had finished speaking they heard the sound of an amazingly brilliant choir. *(After a few seconds, the music stops. The angels take up their place in the tableau around Mary and Joseph)*
Spider	When it stopped the shepherds began to argue with each other about what they had heard, and eventually decided to go to Bethlehem and see the child for themselves.
Shepherd	If this child is so important, why put him in a manger? That's what puzzles me.

All	*Sing 'Away in a Manger'. First verse, children only. Adults join in subsequent verses.*
Narrator	The shepherds were poor, but they were generous. Naturally they wanted to take gifts to the special child. What could they take that was fit for a king? *(The shepherds make their way from the back to place their gifts at the manger)*
Spider	They had no jewels, no fine silk or precious ointment.
Cat	All they had were their own humble skills.
Rat	One collected honey from the hives of wild bees, another wove a rough cloth from wool, and the third made sheep's milk yoghurt.
Narrator	These were the gifts they brought to the stable.
Mouse	At the same time three wise men had been travelling from the East, led by a star, to visit the Holy Family.
Cat	They brought gifts of gold, frankincense and myrrh. But they also sang as they climbed up the hill to Bethlehem. *(The Kings sing the first verse of 'We three Kings', before setting out for Bethlehem in the same way as the shepherds.)*

Narrator	When they saw that everyone was giving presents to the new baby, Simon Spider, Maccabeus Mouse, Reuben Rat and Carmel Cat decided that they would like to give something too. So the spider spun a silken cloth *(Spider walks across stage)*, the mouse juggled *(Mouse takes centre stage)*, the rat danced *(Rat dances)*, and the cat said,
Cat	A manger isn't good enough for Jesus; at least I can make him a proper cradle - a cat's cradle.

(The play ends with the singing of 'The Cat and the Mouse Carol', or another suitable song)

YULETIDE TV NEWS

Characters: Link, Alison, Carol Singer, Innkeeper's Wife, Servant, Joseph, Donkey, Ned Sheepdip, Shepherds 1 and 2, Debbie Tatler, Angels 1 and 2, Angels of the Heavenly Host, Tiggy Euphrates, Melchior, Balthasar, Gaspar, Herod, Theodore Church, Voice Over. (The Donkey and Herod may be played by adults).

The Link (Presenter) should be seated at a desk on a raised platform to one side of the stage. The interviews will happen centre stage. If the production is in church, the producer will use the space available as imaginatively as possible. When they are not involved in the action, young children in the play may be grouped, under adult supervision, to the sides of the acting area.

Every time Yuletide TV is mentioned, its musical theme tune is played.

Dramatic 'ITN' type music as for the 'Ten o'clock News'.

Link	Good evening. This is the news from Yuletide TV *(theme tune)*. Dramatic events have unfolded in the Roman province of Judea. A baby has been proclaimed King of the Jews. Some are saying he is the Son of God. Others that he is the Jewish Messiah.
	But first the news headlines from Alison.
Alison	Thank you, John.
	A child has been born in Bethlehem, Judea. Shepherds found him in a manger after being

tipped off by the Angel of the Lord. He is said to be the 'Saviour'.

Roads have been crowded by people travelling to their home towns to enrol in the census ordered by Caesar Augustus. Congestion is expected to last for a few days.

Astronomers at the Royal Observatory have sighted a strange star. As yet scientists have been unable to give any explanation.

King Herod is said to be furious at reports of the birth of the King of the Jews. John.

Link   Thank you, Alison. For more details of this extraordinary story, let's go over to our staff reporter, Carol Singer, in Bethlehem.

REPORT 1

Carol   Thank you, John. Well, I have with me here the innkeeper's wife from the Starlight Hotel in Bethlehem. Tell me, why did you put important guests in the *stable*?

Wife   Because there was no room in the inn, dear.

Carol   But couldn't you see the woman was going to have a baby?

Wife   Well, it was either the stable, dear, or kipping down on the pavement.

Carol	What's the baby's name?
Wife	Emmanuel, I think.
Servant	*(Standing by)* No it's not, it's Jesus.
Wife	You see, even the servants know more than I do, dear.
Carol	*(Joseph comes forward from the stable)* Now here we have Mary's husband, Joseph. How does it feel to be father of such a special child?
Joseph	Frankly, I've got more than I bargained for. I'm not so young as I used to be, and it's been a long journey from Nazareth. I really didn't expect all this media attention. I just want a bit of privacy for me and my family. I've no further comment.
Carol	But, Mr Joseph, millions of people have been waiting up for a glimpse of the baby. Can you just bring him out for the cameras - and perhaps an angel or two? Then we can leave you in peace.
Joseph	You people are all the same!

(Choir sings, 'When Joseph was an old man' while Mary, Joseph, angels, and baby are presented centre stage.)

Link	I gather you have one more rather special guest.
Donkey	*(Enters stage left)*
Carol	Yes, John, here we have Jeremiah, the donkey who carried Mary from Nazareth to Bethlehem. Good evening Jeremiah?
Donkey	Eeyore.
Carol	How are you?
Donkey	Fed up.
Carol	Why are you fed up?
Donkey	I've had no sleep.
Carol	Why not?
Donkey	Why do you think, you silly goat! They kicked me out of my own bed.
Carol	Who did?
Donkey	Mary, Joseph and - the brat. Then, I'd just got settled outside, and a whole load of shepherds come tramping by, singing and shouting. It's too much for a middle-aged donkey.
Carol	Well, you can sleep all day tomorrow.

Donkey	Hope would be a fine thing. Joseph's been muttering something about Egypt *(pronounced 'Eee-gypt')*.
Link	More on this after the break. But first some music from the heavenly choirs.
All	*(All sing 'While shepherds watched')*

REPORT 2

Link	Welcome back to Yuletide TV. *(Music - a brief snatch of background music, possibly with agricultural theme.)* Our farming correspondent, Ned Sheepdip, has caught up with the shepherds. Hello, Ned.
Ned	Yes, John, it's a starry night here in Bethlehem with a slight frost, which should add sweetness to the turnips. Yes, I can confirm reports that the local shepherds have been to visit Jesus, and here they are with me now.
	Tell me what you saw while you were guarding your flocks in the fields.
Shepherd 1	Well, 'twas an amazing sight. There was all these angels, you see.
Ned	What did the angel say?
Shepherd 2	'Don't be afraid'.

Ned	Anything else?
Shepherd 3	'Have I got good news for you!'
Ned	*(to Shepherd 1)* Yes?
Shepherd 1	'A Saviour is born in the City of David'.
Shepherd 2	'His name is Christ the Lord'.
Ned	*(to shepherd 2)* Go on.
Shepherd 2	'And you'll find him in swaddling clothes'.
Ned	What did you find when you got to the stable?
Shepherd 1	There was this baby, lying in a manger, in the straw.
Ned	Did you take any gifts to the baby?
Shepherds	Yes. A woolly rug, a lamb ...
Ned	Well, thank you very much, Shepherds, and a very merry Christmas to one and all. This is Ned Sheepdip for Yuletide TV, Bethlehem.
Link	Time now for a record. *(The Link announces a carol or song to be sung by all)* sung by the congregation of ... *(Insert the name of the church or school where the play is being performed)*

REPORT 3

(The younger children, especially those with non-speaking parts, are centre stage having a party)

Link   In the last few minutes we have managed to get our court correspondent, Debbie Tatler, into heaven itself for this special report. Debbie.

Debbie   *(In the manner of a reporter's confidential voice-over)*

Thank you, John. Here in heaven the atmosphere is electric with excitement.
(Children explode party popping streamers etc, and release balloons)
The angels, archangels, cherubim and seraphim, and all the heavenly host are in party mood. I have never seen anything like it. This really is a tremendous first for Yuletide TV - and for the World! I am the first reporter ever to be allowed to broadcast from inside the Pearly Gates. I am absolutely overwhelmed by the beauty and exhilaration of this place.
Just look at those angels dance!
(Suitable music is played while the angels dance - such as, 'Glory to God' from Handel's 'Messiah').

Let's find out from the angels what *they* think. Katie, *(or name of child)* what's all the excitement about?

(The angels crowd round - some wave at the camera)

Angel 1   Jesus has been born in Bethlehem.

Debbie   And what's special about Jesus?

Angel 1   He's God's son.

Debbie   Let's ask this angel ... What do you most like about Christmas?

Angel 2   *(Answers in own words.)*

Debbie   Well, I expect you want to get back to your party.

Angels   *(Shouting)* Yes!

Debbie   'Bye, Angels.

Angels   'Bye.

(More party poppers, music, and general excitement)

Debbie   This is Debbie Tatler, Yuletide TV, Heaven - returning you to the studio.

(Short musical interlude)

REPORT 4

Link   Reports are just coming in from Mesopotamia of a giant star. Tiggy Euphrates, our Eastern Correspondent, is there. Good evening, Tiggy.

Tiggy   Good evening, John.

Link   Can you confirm these reports?

Tiggy   Yes, John. There *is* an extraordinary star in the sky which is puzzling local experts. It seems to be moving in the direction of Judea, and it's being followed by three wise men from east of here, who tell me they believe it to be a sign from God. Um ...

Link   This is extraordinary!

Tiggy   Yes, extraordinary, John. I've got the wise men here. Professor Melchior, you first, why follow a star?

Melchior   We believe it will lead us to a heavenly King, who will save the world.

Tiggy   And what have you got wrapped up in these parcels?

Balthasar   They are gifts for the king. I have gold, the sign of a king.

Melchior	I have incense, the sign of holiness.
Gaspar	And I have myrrh, the sign of suffering.
Tiggy	I'm sure all our viewers will want to wish you good luck on your journey. This is Tiggy Euphrates, Yuletide TV, somewhere in Mesopotamia. *(Yuletide theme tune)*
Link	So, another first for Yuletide TV. *(Theme tune)* *(The Kings exit in procession)*
All	*(The congregation sings an appropriate carol)*
	(King Herod comes clambering into the studio, knocking things over as he does so)
Herod	I'll get him. I'll get him. I'll get the little brute. I'm king around here. Let no one forget it. It's not fair. I'm the king for goodness sake.
Link	I'm sorry about this. *(A child holds up a large notice: 'NORMAL SERVICE WILL BE RESUMED AS SOON AS POSSIBLE')*
	King Herod, please sit down. *(He refuses)* Would you like to make a statement?
Herod	Where are those wise men? Take me to the wise men. Schemers, traitors, spies! What a cheek, I ask you, what a cheek. Why is the

whole world against me? I'll get him. I'll get him. Even if I have to kill all the children in Bethlehem. Mark my words, I will.

Children   *(All together)* Boo. Hiss. Get off.

Link   I do apologise for that outrageous outburst. Here's another song from *(name of church or school).*
(All sing a Herod type song - maybe 'Unto us a child is born')

REPORT 5

Link   I've got with me now our religious affairs correspondent, Theodore Church. What do you make of all this, Theodore?

Church   Well, John, I think this baby could just be the Messiah everyone has been waiting for. Remember Isaiah chapter 9, 'For unto us a child is born, unto us a son is given: and the government shall be upon his shoulder: and his name shall be called Wonderful, Counsellor, the mighty God, the everlasting Father, the Prince of Peace.'

I think this will be a very hopeful day for all the poor and afflicted. I understand that Mary, the mother of Jesus, has published a song about the hungry being filled with good things and the rich being sent empty away. Also something about the mighty being put down from their thrones. King Herod won't be pleased about that, I can tell you!

Link   Thank you, Theodore, that's all we have time for tonight. So, from this extended edition of the Ten o'clock news from Yuletide TV, it's goodnight. Goodnight. *(Theme tune)*

(Followed by quiet carol music, while the cast come centre stage to take their bow)

Voice over   Appearing in tonight's edition of Yuletide TV News were: angels of the heavenly host, shepherds in the fields abiding, Joseph and Mary, Jeremiah the Donkey, Three Kings from the Orient, the people of the City of David called Bethlehem, and King Herod himself. Not to mention, our News team: *(give names of children)*.

(End of News music recorded from ITN)

KNOCK, KNOCK, WHO'S THERE?

Characters: (speaking parts) Narrator, King, Bishop, Jester, Queen, Child, Mary, Joseph, First Shepherd, Second Shepherd, Peasant.
(Non-speaking parts) Acolytes, Knights and Ladies. Jesters and Tumblers.
(Before the play begins the audience should be encouraged to join in with the 'knock, knock' jokes.)

SCENE 1
The play begins with a Procession of King, Queen, Bishop (who blesses the people as he proceeds), acolytes, knights and ladies, jesters and tumblers.

Maestoso music while the cast process to the stage. When the children arrive on stage:

Narrator   Let us imagine it is Christmas Day in Medieval
             England, about 600 years ago. The King has
             invited the Bishop, and the courtiers, to a
             celebration in the great hall of his palace. They
             begin by dancing. That is, all except the Bishop,
             who is too pompous.

             *All those on stage dance while they sing the
             following song*

2

Clap hands, give thanks to God
A babe is born, a babe is born.
Clap hands, give thanks to God,
A babe is born to Mary.
Sing together and be merry -
Clap hands, give thanks to God
A babe is born to Mary.

3

Mary sings joyfully,
A babe is born, a babe is born.
Mary sings joyfully,
A babe is born to Mary.
Sing together and be merry -
Mary sings joyfully,
A babe is born to Mary.

King	Come on, Bishop, why be so gloomy on Christmas Day?
Bishop	Are you sure it is not you who are too jolly, Sire?
King	Can't anyone make the Bishop laugh.
Jester	Knock, knock.
All	Who's there?
Jester	Howard
All	Howard who?
Jester	Howard I know? *(All Groan)*
Jester	Knock, knock.
All	Who's there?
Jester	Frank.
All	Frank who?
Jester	*(sings)* Frankincense to offer have I.
Jester	Knock, knock.
All	Who's there?

Jester   Goldy.

All   Goldy who?

Jester   *(sings)* Goldy bring to crown him again.

Jester   Knock, knock.

All   Who's there?

Jester   Esau.

All   Esau who?

Jester   *(sings)* Esau three ships come sailing in.

King   Ho, ho, ho. What a hoot. Come on laugh, my
            Lord Bishop. Someone tickle his feet. This is
            Merry England, figgy pudding, yule logs, and
            all that.

Queen   *(excitedly)*
            I've got one. I've got one.
            Knock, knock.

All   Who's there?

Queen   Lettice.

All   Lettice who?

Queen   Lettice have another carol.

King   Carol who? *(Falls about laughing)*

Jester   Carol Singer!
              (Music of 'I saw three ships' begins to play)

Queen   The one the shipwrights and the sailors used to
              sing.

All   *(sing 'I saw three ships')*

Child   Please Sir, I don't get it. What have three ships
              got to do with Christmas?

Bishop   Father, Son, and Holy Spirit.

Child   So what?

Bishop   The three ships are God, the Father, the Son,
              and the Holy Spirit. We believe that Jesus was
              the Son of God, right?

Child   Yes.

Bishop   So when Jesus was born, it was like God
              sailing into Bethlehem.

King   Oh come on you lot, pass round the sugared
              almonds, and toffee apples, and stop being so
              serious. Everyone must have a glass of
              dandelion and burdock wine.

(While the actors mime eating and drinking, there is music from 'A Merry Christmas' - 'Carols for Choirs' 1, OUP, p 60)

SCENE 2

Narrator   The king was beginning to suffer from a very sharp tummy ache; the trouble was, he was trying too hard to enjoy himself. The more he ate, the worse he felt. And the worse he felt the more the Bishop annoyed him for being so 'sensible'.

King   I'm fed up. Jester you're the only one who can make me laugh. But even your jokes are wearing thin.

Jester   Knock, knock.

All   Who's there?

Jester   Father.

All   Father Christmas?

Jester   No, no, no, no.
Knock, knock.

All   Who's there?

Jester   Father.

All	Father who?
Jester	The farther you go, the less you see.
Bishop	That's deep.
Jester	And the more you learn, the less you know.
King	I wish I knew the secret of Christmas.
Jester	Come on actors. Let us act our Christmas play for the king. Everyone to their places. Quick, quick. Mary, you sit here. Joseph, stand behind her. Look interested, Joseph. Shepherds, are you ready? De, dah. (*He makes the gesture of a magician producing an amazing trick.*)
Mary	Joseph, don't just stand there. I need a clean nappy. There are some in my bag. You've got to learn to do your full share of the work.
Joseph	Yes dear.
	(*A shepherd knocks on the door of the stable, saying:*)
Shepherd	Knock, knock.
Mary	What's all that knocking?
	(*The shepherd repeats the knock*)

Shepherd	Knock, knock.
Joseph	Who's there?
Mary	We can do without your silly jokes now.
Joseph	It's shepherds.
Mary	Shepherds? What can shepherds want with us? Tell them to go away.
Joseph	But they've just seen a vision.
Mary	They're probably drunk - or *(to audience)* after money.
Joseph	No, they say an angel told them to come.
Mary	An *angel*? *(In the manner of 'a handbag!', from 'The Importance of being Earnest')*
First Shepherd	*(pushing his way in)* It's true. We were just nodding off, when it was like fireworks night in the sky, and this voice shouted, 'Don't be afraid! Your saviour has been born in Bethlehem.'
Mary	What did I tell you, Joseph? Our baby *is* special.
Second Shepherd	*(Reluctant to come forward)* Please excuse us, Missis. We are rough men and a bit smelly. We ought not to be here.

Mary   Well, you are here, so you'd better come in.

All   *(sing)*
              It was on a starry night
              When the hills were bright,
              Earth lay sleeping, sleeping calm and still.
              Then in a cattle shed
              In a manger bed,
              A boy was born king of all the world.

              And all the angels sang for him,
              The bells of heaven rang for him,
              For a boy was born king of all the world.
              (repeat these three lines)

              Soon the shepherds came that way
              Where the baby lay
              And were kneeling, kneeling by his side,
              And their hearts believed again
              For the peace of men,
              For a boy was born king of all the world.

              And all the angels sang for him . . .

       (Words and music: Joy Webb. 7 in 'Merrily to Bethlehem')

              SCENE 3

Narrator   The King thought the play was really great,
              and clapped loudly.

King	I wish I could meet this Jesus Christ, this so-called 'King of all the World', then perhaps I'd understand the true meaning of Christmas, and I shouldn't feel so fed up, and shouldn't have to try so hard to enjoy myself. I will give a bag of gold to anyone who can help me to meet Jesus.
Narrator	Then the Bishop stood up.
Bishop	*(Slow and ponderously)* Knock, knock.
King	Oh no, I don't believe it. Bishops don't tell 'knock-knock' jokes.
Bishop	Knock, knock.
All	Who's there?
Bishop	Ivan.
All	Ivan who?
Bishop	Ivan idea. *(All groan)* Christmas is a time for giving, isn't it? I think whoever gives from his heart will see Jesus.
Jester	Great yule logs and Christmas trees, that's it, Sire.
King	Yes, Jester, we all know you're mad!

Jester	Over by the forest fence there's a poor peasant who hardly has two sticks to rub together. He can't even afford bread! Why don't you take him a turkey and some puddings, and join him for Christmas dinner? You know, light a big fire, that sort of thing. Cheer him up. Tell a few jokes. You'll soon discover the true meaning of Christmas.
King	But I can't do that, you fool, I'm the King. And anyway I shall miss the party.
Bishop	There's a bit in the Bible where Jesus says that when you show kindness to others, you show kindness to him.
King	Really? I find that hard to believe.
Bishop	Matthew chapter 25 verse 38, 'Lord, when did we see thee hungry and feed thee ... As you did it to one of the least of these my brethren, you did it unto me.'
Jester	You must do it, Sire.
All	Yes. Please do it, Sire.
King	Oh, very well, then. But if it doesn't work you'll all be locked up in the dungeons, and ... and have to sleep on the slimy floor, and ... and be tickled by spiders.

Narrator   So the next day the King set out with his
            servant to visit the poor peasant who lived by
            the forest fence. As they trudged through the
            snow, the king couldn't help thinking how
            much rather he would be feasting and dancing
            in the great hall of his palace.

            When he came to the peasant's shack, and saw
            how cold and miserable the man really was, he
            was shocked. Never before had he seen
            anything like this, and he began to imagine
            what it would be like not to be a king but a
            beggar instead, shivering and hungry through
            the dark nights of the long winter. The king
            wanted to help him, so he lit a fire, cooked the
            turkey, and they had a great time together.

            Afterwards, on his way home, the king realised
            with surprise how quickly the day had gone,
            and how much more rewarding it had been
            than dancing and telling jokes.

            As he walked he prayed: 'Lord Jesus, I ask only
            one thing, that this Christmas I may meet you,
            just as the shepherds met you at Bethlehem.'
            Then he thought he heard a voice speaking out
            of the darkness. It was the voice of the poor
            peasant:

.Peasant   But you did meet me today - you visited my
            humble house, and brought me food, and we
            ate together. Now do you know the true
            meaning of Christmas?
            (*The king pauses for a moment, then exclaims*)

King   Well, great mince pies and brussels sprouts, I think I jolly well do.

All   (*sing 'Good King Wencelas', with the congregation joining in. At the final verse all come to the front of the stage as a chorus before taking their bow*)

Good King Wenceslas looked out
On the Feast of Stephen,
When the snow lay round about,
Deep and crisp and even:
Brightly shone the moon that night
Though the frost was cruel,
When a poor man came in sight,
Gath'ring winter fuel.

'Hither, page, and stand by me,
If thou know'st it, telling,
Yonder peasant, who is he?
Where and what his dwelling?'
'Sire, he lives a good league hence,
Underneath the mountain,
Right against the forest fence,
By St Agnes' fountain.'

'Bring me flesh and bring me wine,
Bring me pine logs hither:
Thou and I will see him dine,
When we bear them thither.'
Page and monarch, forth they went,
Forth they went together;
Through the rude wind's wild lament
And the bitter weather.

'Sire, the night is darker now,
And the wind blows stronger;
Fails my heart, I know not how; I can go no
longer.'
'Mark my footsteps, good my page;
Tread thou in them boldly:
Thou shallt find the winter's rage
Freeze thy blood less coldly.'

In his master's steps he trod,
Where the snow lay dinted.
Heat was in the very sod
Which the saint had printed.
Therefore, Christian men, be sure,
Wealth or rank possessing,
Ye who now will bless the poor,
Shall yourselves find blessing.

MAK THE THIEF

Characters: Coll, Gib, Daw, (shepherds), Mak (a thief), Gill (Mak's wife), Angel, Mary.

Introductory Note
This play takes its story from the 'Wakefield Second Shepherds' Pageant', which combines a secular story of a sheep stealer with the Nativity of Jesus. The original play is written in poetry, but the language is often difficult for adults, let alone children, to understand.

I have cut the action to its bare bones, and used rhyming couplets to try to catch the poetic flavour. Some of the lines and rhymes come direct from the original. As in the original, I have retained a mixture of comic and serious scenes.

The original was colloquial in style, and I have tried, especially in the comic bits, to catch a modern colloquial idiom.

SCENE 1
(In the fields)

Coll   Lord, my fingers are frozen.
And it's so long since my bed
I feel almost dead.
Out here on the moor
The weather's so raw,
It's no wonder we shepherds are poor.

(Enter Gib, the second shepherd)

37

Gib	Listen to that wind whistle;
	It's as sharp as a thistle.
	I tell you this, it's a hard life -
	Especially if you're married to my wife!
	You know my advice to all young men?
	If you're thinking of marrying - then think
	again.
Coll	Gib, have you seen Daw anywhere?
Gib	I thought I heard him over there.
	Let's hide.
Daw	*(Enters rubbing hands to keep warm)*
	This weather must be the worst since Noah's
	flood.
	Let's pray God will use it for some good.
	(Confiding to audience)
	We who guard our sheep at nights
	Sometimes see the strangest sights:
	Creatures of all shapes and sizes,
	Bringing good and bad surprises.
	I'm sure I saw two rascals behind the hedge.
	(He jumps on Coll and Gib)
Coll	Get off, you idiot, or I'll have you whipped.
Daw	Oh, oh. It's you, masters, I must have slipped.
	(Winks at audience)

Gib	Surely, you haven't left the sheep alone?
Daw	Relax! Nothing can go wrong.
Coll	He's right. By heavens, these nights are long! *(To Gib)* Why not sit and give us a song? *(They sing verses from the Sans Day Carol, 'Now the holly bears a berry'.)* *(Mak arrives, he is wearing a cloak stolen from Daw.)*
Gib	Mak, where have you come from? What tidings?
Daw	Is that Mak? Be careful, everyone, and watch your things.
Mak	I'm a perfect gentleman. A thief? What me? One day I'll get the OBE. You'll see.
	(They all laugh and point at him)
Gib	The OBE, ha, ha.
Coll	The OBE, oh yes!
Daw	Pull the other one!
Coll	Well, I'll tell you something funny; Last time I met Mak, I lost my money.
Gib	And, if you really want a joke, Last time I met Mak, I lost my cloak. *(He whips the cloak from Mak's back and holds it up.)*

Daw It makes you wonder who's the creep
That roams these hills stealing sheep.

Coll, Gib *(To each other, and looking at Mak)*
and Daw Yes. I wonder! Who can it be?

Mak *(Wildly protesting)*
That's slander, lies, and porky pies.
(To audience)
It's the honest truth - look in my eyes.

Coll How's your wife, then, Mak? How's Gill?

Mak Ooh! I'm afraid she's ill.
Too many kids to feed on my pay,
And always another one on the way.

Gib Well, it's time for bed, I'd say.
I shan't be counting sheep tonight.
As soon as my head hits the hay,
I'll be out like a light.

Daw Mak, you lie here between Gib and me.
You'll feel safer there, and so will we.

*(They go to sleep and Mak pretends to snore loudly.
Quiet music plays. He gets up and checks the others
are asleep)*

Mak *(Casts a spell to make them stay asleep)*
Abracadabra, jumping Jack.
Don't wake up till I come back.

(To audience)
Now's the time for me to be bold
And get a bargain from the fold.
Oh, come on! It can't be wrong!
Those shepherds aren't going to miss just *one*.
(Audience can be encouraged to hiss)

(He exits, and after a pause shouts)
There! Gotcha!

(He returns on stage carrying a sheep)
This was the fattest sheep on the hill.
I can't wait to show it to Gill.

(He exits)

SCENE 2
(Inside Gill's cottage. She is sitting beside a cradle)

Mak	Hello Gill. Are you there? Give me some light.
Gill	Who's making that din at this time of night?
Mak	Open the door and see what I've brought.
Gill	*(Opens the door and when she sees the sheep she is shocked)* You'll hang by the neck if you get caught.

Mak	Why shouldn't a poor man eat? We're entitled to have meat, So don't get in such a flap - Anyway, it just fell into my lap!
Gill	Yeah, right! As if! I believe you; thousands wouldn't. Try the judge - He'll say you shouldn't.
Mak	Oh, shut up. This is going to be a real treat.
Gill	What if the shepherds come, and hear it bleat?
Mak	Heavens! You're right. Then I'll be for it. *(Feebly)* Help, help. Whatever shall we do? They're bound to beat me black and blue.

(They both think, and scratch their heads)

Gill	I've thought of a good trick - Since you're so thick. It's only a little fib; We'll hide him in this crib.
Mak	Yes, yes, yes, brilliant, right - I'll say you had a kid last night. *(They shake hands)*
Gill	But you must go back and pretend to sleep Or they'll think it was you Who stole their sheep. *(Winks at audience).*

SCENE 3
(Back in the fields Mak and the shepherds lie asleep)

Coll   *(Waking and stretching)*
        What a bad night; I'm still feeling grumpy;
        The grass was like wire
        And the ground was all lumpy.

Gib   *(Jumping up)*
        Well, I feel as fresh as a daisy. *(Does fitness exercises)*

Daw   *(Wakes up shaking, but doesn't see Mak)*
        I've had a dream that will make you both crazy.
        I dreamt I saw Mak, as a wolf in disguise,
        Steal a sheep from our fold to make mutton pies.

Gib   Don't be stupid, Daw.
        Mak's here on the floor.
        Wake up, Mak. What will your mother say
        If you lie in bed all day?

Mak   Now praise to Almighty God,
        I slept like a yuletide log!
        In fact, my muscles feel so pinched,
        I bet I never moved an inch.
        I had a dream as weird as may be;
        I dreamt that Gill had had a baby:
        Giving birth at four o'clock -
        a young lad to add to our flock!

I must go home to see how she's been:
(Stands with arms outstretched in order to be frisked)
Frisk me first to check I'm clean. *(He goes)*

Daw   Good riddance.
I think we had better count our sheep.

Coll   And then we'll all meet.

Gib   Where?

Daw   At the crooked thorn.

Interlude: a carol may be sung between Scenes 3 and 4

SCENE 4
(Mak's cottage. Gill is seated. Mak knocks at the door)

Mak   Open the door. It's me. I'm back.

Gill   *(Opens door. To audience)* It's him, old good-for-nothing Mak!

Mak   *(Pointing to sheep)* Not as useless as you claim!

Gill   Did the shepherds suspect your game?

Mak   The last thing they said before I left:
They'd count their sheep in case of theft.
Whichever way the cookie's crumbled,
You can bet that I'll be rumbled.

Gill	Then there'll be all hell let loose; Those bumkins'll have your neck in a noose.
Mak	You must do as you promised.
Gill	We'll do as I said. I'll wrap him in this little bed. *(She wraps the sheep in swaddling clothes)* You take a blanket and cover his head. As soon as they come - they won't be long - You must sing a cradle-song. I'll lie on the bed and groan, And if he bleats or makes a moan, Say it was the telephone. *(Exit)*

SCENE 5
(The crooked thorn)

Daw	*(Meeting Gib and Coll, who are looking exceedingly glum)* Ah Coll, You look as mad as a parent who can't get its own way.
Coll	So will you when you hear what I've got to say. Someone has stolen our best sheep today.
Daw	Who'd play a dirty trick like that?
Gib	I'd like to catch the little brat.

Daw	I'll bet five quid it's Gill or Mak.
Coll	How could it be that little cuss? If you recall, he slept with us.
Gib	Nothing's ever guaranteed, I'm sure it's Mak that did this deed; And if he wasn't thereabouts, I'll eat my Christmas brussels sprouts.
All Three	(*Shouting*) Let's find him! We'll get him! (*Exit*)

SCENE 6
(*Mak's cottage. Gill is in bed groaning, Mak is singing - very badly and coarsely - the 'Coventry Carol' refrain, the shepherds approach and hear the noise.*)

Mak	Lully, lulla, thou little tiny child, By by, lully lullay, Thou little tiny child, By by, lully lullay
Daw	Listen how our cock likes to croon!
Coll	Even a frog would sing more in tune.
Gib	Open up, Mak. It's us: Gib, Daw, and Coll.
Mak	(*Opens door*) Hush! Shoosh! Gill's not very well.
Gill	No. Clear off. I feel rather wuzzy; Come back tomorrow, or better, on Thursday.

Mak	I'm sorry. Whatever must you think? Come and sit down. I'll get a drink, *(pointing to the cradle)* And we can toast the new born kiddy, Which has made poor Gill so giddy.
Daw	No thanks. *(Accusingly)* A sheep's been stolen from our herd.
Mak	Good grief!
Daw	And we are looking for the thief.
Mak	*(All bravado and posing like a boxer)* If I'd been there, he'd not be free; He'd have got a right bashing from me!
Coll	*(Looking at other shepherds and getting their agreement)* Some people think that *you* were *he*.
Mak	What me? You really must be jesting. I don't like what you're suggesting. Search our house from top to bottom; We certainly haven't got 'im.
Gill	*(They begin to search. Coll approaches the cradle)* Help. Thieves. Robbers. Kidnappers! *(Everyone turns to look at Gill)*
Mak	Take no notice. I think she's crackers.

(Coll approaches the cradle again.)

Gill   Get those brutes away from his cot.

Mak   *(Feeling Gill's brow)*
Do as she says - her temper's hot.

(Coll tries to look into the cradle)

Gill   *(Screams)* Ah, my middle.
I swear by God so mild
If I have you beguiled
That I shall *eat* this child.

All   *(With some irony)* Aaah!

             (The shepherds complete their search)
Gib   I've found nothing, how about you?

Daw   Nothing here. We may as well go.
But I tell you: Sure as hell,
This baby has a funny smell.

(Mak shakes hands with the shepherds and they go. Gill gets up, and she and Mak congratulate themselves. But the shepherds have second thoughts and have paused outside.)

Coll   Did you leave anything for the boy?

Gib   No. Not even a cuddly toy.

Daw	Well, we had better go back in. *(They barge back into the cottage. Offering money)* Ah, Mak. Here's something for your son.
Mak	No! Go away! He sleeps.
Daw	I think he peeps.
Mak	No he doesn't.
Daw	*(Approaching the cradle)* I'll lift up the quilt and give him a kiss. He has a long snout: what the devil is this?
Gib	He's just like our sheep.
Coll	Let me have a peep.
Daw	You fraud, you freak, you rotten goose; You'll hang for this. Bring me the noose.
Gill	No wait! Relax. I can explain - And, no, I'm really not insane: Our babe was taken by an elf - I saw it come and go myself. At twelve o'clock my watch went 'beep', Lo and behold - our boy's a sheep!
Coll	You must think we're soft in the head; You took our sheep, and now you're dead. *(They toss Mak in a blanket)*

SCENE 7
(In the fields)

Coll   Well, I'm glad that's done.

Gib   Poor old Mak, he weighed a ton.

Daw   We all need sleep, so let's lie down.

      (They lie down to go to sleep. After a pause the music of the 'Sussex Carol' begins to play, then the first verse is sung by choir or congregation.)

Angel   *(From on high)*
Rise up, good shepherds, for now is he born
Who brings new life to all forlorn.
He is God's own son, so blow your horn,
And praise him on this Christmas morn.

You shall go to Bethlehem and see,
The child who makes all people free,
Humbly wrapped in poverty.
(The shepherds get up and look at the sky)

Daw   Great woolly jumpers! Do I lie?
An angel speaking from the sky?

Gib   And why should we be first to know?
Poor shepherds - lowest of the low?

Coll   What was that song? How did it run?

Gib	*(Tries the tune)* De dum, de dum, de dum diddy dum . . .
Daw	On Christmas night, all Christians sing To hear the news the angels bring.
Coll	News of great joy, news of great mirth, News of our merciful King's birth.
Gib	In Bethlehem he said he'd be. Let's get our bags and go and see. *(They exit)*

(More verses of the 'Sussex Carol' are sung.)

SCENE 8
(The stable in Bethlehem)

Coll	Hail, comely and clean; hail young child! Hail, heavenly King so mild. Look how he laughs and merries. I have brought a bunch of cherries.
Gib	Hail, sovereign saviour, blest Messiah, Virgin-born, as said Isaiah. *(Cooing)* Yes, it *is* tremendous sport, To see the bird that I have brought?
Daw	Hail, thou Wisdom from on high! Who madest all in earth and sky:

I have no wealth or mansion tall;
I bring thee but a tennis ball.
(He bounces the ball)

(Mak enters - the others look at him disgusted)

Gib, Coll and Daw	Who let *him* in here?
Mary	*(Gestures to them to be silent)*
Mak	Hail, to the one who brings relief;
	Can you forgive a wicked thief?
	I'm sorry - all my money's spent -
	I have no gift, but I repent.
Mary	The God of Heaven, the Holy One,
	Who made all life, has sent his Son,
	And by his grace has chosen me
	The mother of our Lord to be.

So now I pray his holy birth
May bring good will and peace on earth
To everyone: friends, enemies, relations -
To men and women of all nations.

And as you go upon your way,
Remember what you've seen today,
And what you heard the angels say,
That Christ is Lord and rules, OK.

CHRISTMAS CABARET

Introductory Note

The 'Christmas Cabaret' is intended as an improvisation for three adult actors and a reader. There is a box of props on stage which the actors take one by one and improvise with them on a Christmas theme - along the lines of the TV programme, 'Whose line is it anyway'.

The aim is to produce a show that is like pantomime, or street theatre. Experience has shown that this will hold the attention of even very young children.

The basic idea can be adapted to suit local needs and resources. For example, the musical interludes can use whatever musical talent is available, and can themselves be like cabaret items. It helps to have someone who can perform a few basic conjuring tricks, but any form of children's entertainment could be used.

Children from the audience should be included in the action wherever possible. For example, to play the parts of sheep, wise men, and conjurer's assistants.

Improvisation isn't easy, and it may be helpful to develop a script in the course of rehearsals. The text that follows was written in advance, and developed by the actors in three rehearsals. It was performed at a Christmas Eve Children's Crib Service

Most of the props came from home, but paper crowns, sheep and donkey masks, red nose, and the jester's hat came from the local party shop for fifteen pounds. The props are kept in a large box, centre stage, so that they can be picked up as needed.

Cast

ACTOR 1
ACTOR 2
ACTOR 3 *(who must be female).*
READER

The actors should wear brightly coloured and unusual clothes to add a sense of theatre and excitement.

Properties list:

Jester's hat
3 conjuring tricks
A shepherd's staff
2 sheep masks
A doll
A lantern (to hang on staff)
2 woolly hats and 2 woolly scarves
Pair of sunglasses
A donkey mask
Some holly
A plastic red nose
A very large cardboard box
A mixing bowl, wooden spoon, and mince pie
A shopping bag containing: perfume, bath salts, and a gaudy tie
Binoculars
3 cardboard crowns
3 colourful boxes containing sweets

ENTRANCE OF THE ACTORS

(The company enters from the back of the church or auditorium singing a medieval dance carol. They arrive on the stage)

Actor 1   *(as Jester)* Roll up, roll up to the Christmas Cabaret. Take your seats, ladies and gentlemen, please. Pray silence for the entertainers. Ladies and gentlemen, may I present to you ... *(Name of Reader)*. *(Encourages applause from the audience)*. Ladles and jellyspoons, may I present to you, the wondrous antipodean, Madame Suzanne *(Name of Actor 3)*. Children and parents, grandparents and aunties, I give you the amazing Balthazar *(Actor 2)*, magician from the East.

Actor 2   *(as Balthazar - one of the Kings - performs his first conjuring trick - e.g. the magic wooden block on a rope, which stops only when the correct magic words are spoken. Balthazar, naturally, talks to the audience as he performs his magic.)*

Actor 1   Finally, my Lords, ladies and Christmas turkeys, I present myself, a man of jest and changing faces.

SEQUENCE ONE

(Actor 2 throws a staff to the Actor 1, who removes his hat and becomes an old shepherd)

Actor 1   (*In 'country bumpkin' voice*) I be an 'umble
           shepherd. But where are my sheep? I have lost
           my sheep.
           (*Actor 2 and 3 appear as sheep, making baaing
           noises*)
           But I thought I had more sheep than that.
           (*Pointing to audience*) Have some of them
           strayed out there? (*Invites children to be sheep.
           Gets them to baa. Gets the audience to baa.*)

           Well, it was like this you see. Last night we
           were in the fields, and suddenly there was a
           great, blinding light in the sky, and I fell on my
           knees in fear. Then this voice there, says, 'Glory
           to God in the highest, and peace to all people
           of good will. Be not afraid,' he says, 'Behold I
           bring you good tidings of great joy, which shall
           be to all people. For unto you is born this day
           in the City of David, a Saviour who is Christ
           the Lord. And you will know when you see
           him because he will be wrapped in swaddling
           clothes, and lying in a manger.'

           (*Throws staff to Actor 2, who now plays Joseph.
           Actor 3, as Mary, is holding the doll. They act being
           a dad and mum.*)

Actor 2   I'm a dad! And this is my wife, Mary.

Actor 3   Hello, everybody. (*Showing the doll*) Isn't he
           lovely?

Actor 2	Guess what his name is. *(Waits for audience response)* That's right, Jesus. *(To Actor 3)* It's nice in this little stable, isn't it?
Actor 3	It could be worse, I suppose. *(To audience)* I said to him, I said. You have to book, you know. Christmas is a busy time; if you want a hotel, you have to book. But would he book? Oh no. It'll be all right, he said. There'll be plenty of room ...
Actor 2	Oh, stop rabbitting, dear. *(Listens)* I think I can hear someone coming. *(Throws staff to Actor 1 who tells the rest of the story.)*
Actor 1	So I said to my sheep - where are my sheep? Baa, to show me where you are. So I said, let us go even unto Bethlehem and see this thing that has come to pass. And we found Mary and Joseph, and the babe lying in a manger. And I told Mary and Joseph what the angel had said, how Jesus was the Messiah, Christ the Lord, and they were amazed. And Mary said that she couldn't say anything now, but that she would be pondering these things in her heart. *(Actors 2 and 3 dress Actor 1 as a carol singer, and hang a lantern on his staff)*

Actor 1   The carol singers, or waits, used to dress like this when they went singing from house to house. In medieval England a 'carol' was a dance, like the one we sang when we came in. *(Music of 'Ding, Dong, merrily on high' strikes up)*

The one we're going to sing now is a French dance-carol. 'Ding, Dong, merrily on high'.

(The company on stage sing as carol singers)

SEQUENCE TWO

Actor 3   *(as New Zealander)* What else have we got in here? Sun glasses! *(Puts them on)* An oil sheikh from the East? Or I could be at home, enjoying a day on the beach.

Actor 2   *(enters wearing the donkey mask, and making a clip-clopping sound)*
Hey, Suzanne *(ie Actor 3)*. *(Confiding to the audience)* I like hay. Hey, Suzanne. What do you do on Christmas Day in New Zealand?

Actor 3   Well, it's not winter all round the world at Christmas, you know. In New Zealand, after I've been to church, I go for a barbecue on the beach.

Actor 1   *(In normal voice as Jester)* It must be strange singing 'In the bleak mid winter' in the middle of summer.

Actor 3   Well, we do sing your old favourites, and some of our own as well.

Actor 1   Do you have holly and ivy?

Actor 3   Sometimes, but we have a marvellous tree called the 'pohutakawa', with wonderful red flowers, that reminds us of Christmas. *(Exits)*

Actor 2   *(Throws holly to Actor 1)* Hey, catch this, Jester.

Actor 1   Ouch! That hurts. Did you know, in Norway and Sweden holly is known as the 'Christ Thorn' Why? Because the prickles could make a crown of thorns. The white flowers (did you know holly has white flowers?) remind us of the purity of the Virgin Mary. And the red berries are like drops of blood, which remind us of Jesus' death on the cross. Remember the carol about the holly and the ivy: 'Now the holly bears a berry, as red as any blood, and Mary bore sweet Jesus Christ, to do poor sinners good'?
            (Throws holly back to Actor 2) Here, Donkey, you can have this back.

Actor 2   Ouch!

Actor 3   *(Taking red nose from box)* Now What's this?

Actor 2   A jolly big berry, Suzanne!

Actor 3   *(Puts it on)* This shouldn't be here. *(Acts drunk)* Dad's drunk the brandy for the Christmas pudding? What does it remind you of, children? *(Children shout out ideas. Actor 3 ad libs in response to their suggestions)* Who else has a red nose? Rudolph?

(Actors 1 and 2 start to sing - all join in)

Rudolph the red nosed reindeer
Had a very shiny nose

(The actors come front of stage and sing with rhythmic dance movements)

And if you ever saw him
You would really think it glows.
All of the other reindeers
Used to laugh and call him names
They never let poor Rudolph
Join in any reindeer games.

Then one foggy Christmas Eve
Santa came to stay,
Rudolph with your nose so bright
Won't you guide my sleigh tonight?

Then how the reindeers loved him,
They all shouted out with glee:
Rudolph the Red nosed Reindeer
You'll go down in history.

Actor 2   What shall we do now?

Actor 1   I know. I've got one. *(He begins to mime a charade for 'Jingle Bells'. The others guess:)*

Company   Song. Two words. Second word, sounds like *(he holds his nose)* smells. Sounds like, smells. First word *(he jangles the bells on his hat)* jangle. Jangle smells?
Jingle Bells.

Actor 2   I've got one. *(He mimes 'Little Donkey')*

Company   Two words. First word. *(Uses his hands to indicate smallness)* A? The? Small? Little? Second word. *(Donkey makes his 'clip-clop' noise and gallops round stage)*

Company   Donkey? Little Donkey.

(Musical interlude on tune of 'Little Donkey', or choice)

(During this, Actors 1 and 2 place cardboard box centre stage, as if they were scenery removers)

SEQUENCE THREE

Actor 3   Hello, what's this box for? It so big! If you were lucky it might contain your Christmas present. But if I put it on the ground, it's just big enough for me and the baby Jesus to sit inside.

That makes me think of all the homeless people who have to sleep outside in the cold weather.

(Gives box to Actor 1)

Actor 1   It reminds me of something different. Can anybody guess? What about the day after Christmas? Boxing day. Why do you think it's called Boxing Day?

In the Middles Ages - a very long time ago - the priests used to open the poor boxes, where people had put money for the poor, and distributed the money to those in need - hence, Boxing Day.

Actor 2   *(Now as Balthazar) (Holding a mixing bowl and wooden spoon)* One of the good things about Christmas is food. What are your favourite Christmas foods? *(Audience makes suggestions)* I'm making mince pies. Well, here's one I made earlier. I need a volunteer from the audience to came and test it. *(Calls up a child from the audience).* But there's one condition: you've got to tell me what you think about as you eat it! *(Volunteer eats the pie and answers the question)*

Did you know that mince pies used to be made in shape of a cradle? People were supposed to eat them quietly and think of the Lord Jesus Christ. *(Actor 2 gives a wry nod of the head and a wink to the audience)*

(Reader comes on stage during Actor 3's next speech)

Actor 3   *(Taking shopping bag)* I've just finished my Christmas shopping. What have we here? Perfume - who shall I give that to? *(Actor 3 ad libs in response to audience suggestions).* Bath salts - who shall I give them to? And this very gaudy tie - who shall I give that to?

Reader   That reminds me of John Betjeman's poem 'Christmas' - or, at least, the last three verses.

'And is it true? And is it true,
This most tremendous tale of all,
Seen in a stained-glass window's hue,
A baby in an ox's stall?
The Maker of the stars and sea
Become a Child on earth for me?

And is it true? For if it is,
No loving fingers tying strings
Around those tissued fripperies,
The sweet and silly Christmas things,
Bath salts and inexpensive scent
And hideous tie so kindly meant,

No love that in a family dwells,
No carolling in frosty air,
Nor all the steeple-shaking bells
Can with this single Truth compare -
That God was Man in Palestine
And lives to-day in Bread and Wine.'

(Musical interlude)

SEQUENCE FOUR

Actor 3   *(Taking binoculars)* Oh, look at that. What a beautiful star.

Actor 2   *(Wearing a crown)* Oh thanks. I've been looking for that. *(ie the star!)*

Hello children, I am Balthazar, one of the wisest of wise men. But where are my friends, Melchior and Gaspar? *(Calls up two members of the audience, and places crowns on their heads)* See how wise Melchior and Gaspar are. Yet I am even wiser because I can do magic. Stand back and behold. *(Performs other two conjuring tricks, and asks assistants to verify that genuine materials are being used)*

But we have more serious business than this. We have been following this star for about ten days now. We lost it for a while when the sky got cloudy, but now we've found it again. We are following it to a place where we shall find a king even greater than the three of us - can you believe it? We had better get on our way.

Actor 3   Haven't you forgotten something? There are three more things in the box. *(She produces three boxes of sweets, wrapped as gold, frankincense, and myrrh. She gives them to the wise men)*

Actor 3   While the wise men take their gifts to Jesus, we shall sing, 'We three kings of orient are'.

Audience   'We three kings'
sings
      (The kings move slowly around the stage, or church, or hall, bearing their gifts, and as their particular verse is sung they lay their gifts before Actor 3/ Mary, who holds the doll/Jesus)

Actor 1   That's it folks. Happy Christmas to everyone.

The Cast   *(Line up to take a bow, open the gold, frankincense, and myrrh, and throw sweets into the audience.*

      Exit, singing carol)